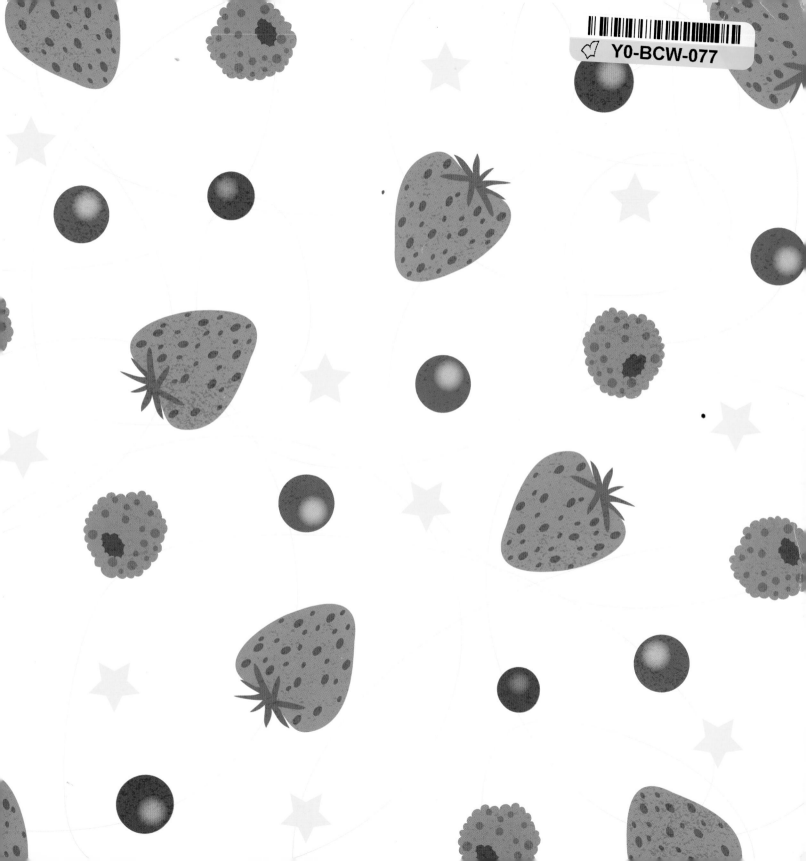

sneaky spinach

BY ALEXIS SCHULZE ★ ART BY SOPHIE HANTON

Copyright Information
ISBN: 9780692768679
Library of Congress Control Number: 2016913440

Copyright 2016 Alexis Schulze
Illustrations by Sophie Hanton
Book Design by Emily O'Malley

Book production services by
CardinalRulePress.com

First Printing 2016
All rights reserved.
Printed in the United States of America

Schulze, Alexis (1974-)
Sneaky Spinach

1. Nutrition 2. Health 3. Wellness 4. Relationships
5. Family Life

Néktər Juice Bar
1844 E. Carnegie Avenue
Santa Ana, CA 92705
nekterjuicebar.com

Special acknowledgments to our Néktər
Juice Bar team for supporting our mission
and bringing Sneaky Spinach to life every
day in our stores.

And to those in my life who are no longer
with me – your love has always inspired me
and I hope I make you proud.

DISCUSSION QUESTIONS

BEFORE READING:

★ Read the title aloud, emphasizing the word "sneaky". Ask your child what the word "sneaky" means. Have they ever seen anyone act that way?

★ Look at the vegetables on the front cover. Encourage your child to name them. Which do they like and dislike?

DURING READING:

★ Does your child know what a blender is? Talk to them about it and describe its function and the sound it makes.

★ Keep track of how many different ways the spinach helps Nick.

AFTER READING:

★ Name three different ways the smoothie helped Nick.

★ Did you notice a little bumblebee throughout the book? Go back and search the pages for it!

MORE LEARNING:

★ Take your child on a field trip to the grocery store. Help them pick out ingredients to make the smoothie recipes in this book.

★ Are there any juice bar locations in your area? If so, visit one and enjoy a healthy smoothie with your family.

★ Gather old magazines or newspapers. Ask your child to cut out pictures and sort them into one of two categories: healthy foods and not healthy foods.

This book is dedicated to
all of the children in my life.
A child's perspective on life is such
a gift. Especially my two boys – there
is no greater love. To Steve – for always
being willing to grow. To my mom – for
making me eat my veggies!

— AS —

For my lovely parents, who are
a positive and loving force in my
life, thank you, my best friends. For
my supportive husband Mark, thank you.
For my two beautiful boys, Sam and Oli, who
make me smile every day with their love for
life, I love you always, boys, you amazing
little people.

— SH —

Nick loves to eat junk food. His three favorite foods are cookies, soda and chips. Because he eats so poorly, Nick is always sick and tired.

His mom is always telling him to eat more vegetables so he can be healthier. Nick is sick and tired of hearing that, too.

But everyone knows that fruits and vegetables are great for you! And nobody knows that better than vegetables themselves!

On Sunday, Nick's mom worked really hard to make a healthy dinner for the family. Everyone enjoyed the dinner – except for Nick.

He crossed his arms and grunted. "I am not going to eat any spinach, and you can't make me!" Nick was sent to his room.

That night, the spinach leaves got to thinking, *"How can we make sure Nick eats his veggies?"* After talking it over, they came up with a plan.

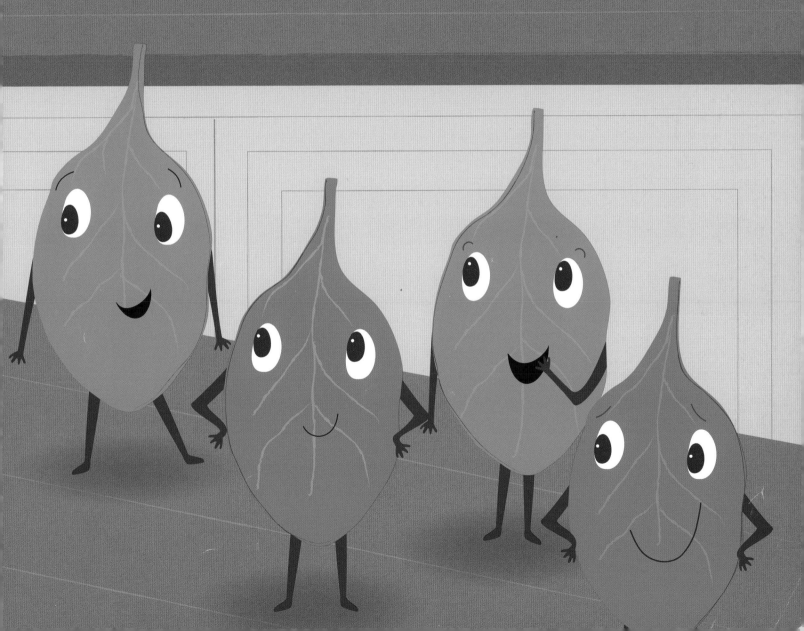

On Monday, Nick and his mom made his morning smoothie together. They put frozen berries, milk, and a banana into the blender. Meanwhile, three spinach leaves crept across the counter, dove into the blender, and disappeared. Nick never saw those sneaky little spinach leaves, and he drank the whole thing!

That day at school, Nick felt strong and full of energy! He even felt fast enough to tag Donovan, the fastest kid on the playground.

On Tuesday, Nick and his mom made his morning smoothie together. They put frozen berries, milk, and a banana into the blender. Meanwhile, four spinach leaves crept across the counter, dove into the blender, and disappeared. Nick never saw those sneaky little spinach leaves, and he drank the whole thing!

That day at school, Nick did better on his test than ever before. He even spelled more words correctly than that smarty-pants, Sara. He was feeling like a smarty-pants himself and he liked it!

On Wednesday, Nick and his mom made his morning smoothie together. They put frozen berries, milk, and a banana into the blender. Meanwhile, five spinach leaves crept across the counter, dove into the blender, and disappeared. Nick never saw those sneaky little spinach leaves, and he drank the whole thing!

That day at school, Nick felt better
than ever. He even did more pull ups
than Bobby, the strongest kid at school.

On Thursday, Nick and his mom made his morning smoothie together. They put frozen berries, milk, and a banana into the blender. Meanwhile, six spinach leaves crept across the counter, dove into the blender, and disappeared. Nick never saw those sneaky little spinach leaves, and he drank the whole thing!

That day at school, everyone in class was acting crazy. They were talking loud and forgetting to listen. But Nick felt completely focused.

On Friday, Nick and his mom made his morning smoothie together. They put frozen berries, milk, and a banana into the blender. Meanwhile, seven spinach leaves crept across the counter. But this time, because Nick was so much faster, smarter, stronger and calmer, he caught those seven sneaky spinach leaves before they could jump into the blender.

"Hey! What do you think you're doing?" he yelled.

The bravest spinach leaf proudly said, "We have been sneaking into your smoothie all week to make you healthier."

Nick exclaimed, "So *that's* why all those special things happened this week. The spinach in my smoothie gave me super powers!"

Now, Nick was so smart that he decided to put spinach in his smoothie every day. He wanted to keep feeling great. "Vegetables aren't so bad after all," he told his mom, "And in a smoothie, I can't even taste them!"

"That's because we're so sneaky!"
the super spinach leaves cheered.

This is Nick's favorite smoothie. Its bright color is bursting with delicious flavor and antioxidants. Sweeten to taste by adding more fruit or agave nectar. Blend well and enjoy!

16 OZ. BERRY BANANA BURST

5 frozen strawberries
1/2 cup frozen blueberries
1/2 frozen banana
1.5 teaspoon agave nectar
8 ounces of 2% reduced fat or 1% skim milk
    (or milk alternative)
    + Sneaky Spinach: add 3-8 spinach leaves

Blend until all fruit is combined.

(355 Calories, 6g Total Fat, 3g Sat Fat, 47 g Total Sugar, 7 g Added Sugar)

5 TIPS FOR MAKING A GREAT SMOOTHIE

1. *Start small...as the spinach did in the book.* **One or two leaves is better than nothing. If you add too much, children may notice and then your cover is blown. You can slowly work your way into adding more.**

2. *Include your child:* **Have your child help you make the smoothie. Have fun with it and be prepared to "doctor" it with more of something, but make them think it's their idea or give them choices so they are fully taking ownership of the smoothie.**

3. *Sneak in the goods:* **If your child is older, they may already have an idea of what the spinach tastes like, so you will need to have some sneaky moves of your own. I recommend adding the spinach at the bottom so it gets blended in really well.**

4. *Use frozen fruit:* **Frozen fruits make a smoothie thick without being icy. Bananas are great additions frozen or fresh, either way they make it creamy and sweet. Always use fresh baby spinach – they are mild in flavor and blend best.**

5. *Have fun and experiment:* **A good thing to remember is that the worst experimental smoothie can always have more sweet stuff added to make it taste better.**

Combining her passion for both children and healthy living, Alexis Schulze wrote Sneaky Spinach to encourage kids of all ages to eat nutritiously to fuel more active and happy lives. In her role as Co-Founder and Chief Visionary Officer of Nékter Juice Bar, a modern lifestyle brand devoted to empowering communities to pursue well-being, Alexis leads the company's efforts to create delicious, nutrient-rich menu items, sneaking in spinach as much as possible.

In addition to founding Nékter with her husband in 2010, Alexis has over 20 years of experience working with children in both preschool and elementary school settings. She holds a Bachelor's Degree in Child and Adolescent Development, a Master's Degree in Cross-Cultural Education and recently completed her Health Coach Certification. She lives in Orange County, California, with her husband, Steve, and their two boys, Bobby and Donovan, who, through *Sneaky Spinach*, have learned to love their fruits and vegetables.

From a very young age, Sophie Hanton always had a pencil, crayon, or paintbrush in her hand. She always knew she would follow a creative path. After graduating with a BA (Hons) Surface Pattern from Staffordshire University, she completed various design projects while freelancing. Later joining a busy design studio, producing wraps, tags, bags and boxes for all areas of the market. She gained lots of computer aided design experience, and blossomed as a designer.

Over ten years ago, she decided to become a self-employed freelance designer/ artist/illustrator. This has allowed her to broaden her experience in widely varying projects. She has illustrated a number of books, designed toys, puzzles and logos and also designed for the tabletop, fabrics and greetings market. Sophie sees every brief as a new challenge and always does her best to meet it, knowing how lucky she is to be doing a job that she is so passionate about. Sophie lives in beautiful Cornwall in the UK, and spends her free time swimming in the sea and having fun on the beach.